HOLY HEROES® **Jesse Tree**

HISTORY OF SALVATION

Day-by-Day Advent Activities

"There shall come forth a shoot from the stump of Jesse,
and a branch shall grow out of his roots.
And the Spirit of the Lord shall rest upon him ..."

ISAIAH 11:1-2

Enter into the richness of Salvation History this Advent!

These faith-filled **Jesse Tree Activities** are brought to you by the ***Holy Heroes Adventure Guides!***

Caroline

Lillian

Therese

Anna

Trey

Margaret

Clara

Virginia

This activity book was compiled and edited, including new daily activities devised and created, by Therese Davison

ISBN 978-1-936330-81-2 Printed in the U.S.A.

Make this your best Advent ever!

In addition to these fun **Jesse Tree Activities,** here are **TWO MORE** FUN Advent activities!

① Register for our FREE catechetical journey to Christmas!

Learn from the Holy Heroes *"Adventure Guides"* & *"Answer Kid,"* too!

We do all the work for you, sending you daily emails full of fun:

- Prepare your heart for Jesus through our **Sacrifice Manger activity!**
- Make family memories as you explore **Advent Traditions and Feast Days** together!
- Get more out of the Mass with **"Mass prep" activities for each Sunday** of Advent!
- Fall in love with the **Rosary**. Pray a "decade-a-day" and get "rosary certified" this Advent!

Fun, Faithful and FREE activities all through ADVENT ... Register NOW at

www.AdventAdventure.com!

② Start a new family tradition—make your own Advent candles!

Advent Candles and an Advent Wreath are fun ways to focus on preparing our hearts for the celebration of the first coming of Jesus Christ into the world as a little baby on Christmas morning!

Our Advent Candle Kit is easy for kids ages 6 & up—and Moms and Dads, too!
Each kit makes four 8" tapered candles (3 violet and 1 rose) from 100% pure beeswax. The candles are very easy to make, smell heavenly when burned, and are sure to delight you children all Advent long. The kit also includes a detailed information sheet on the beautiful symbolism of beeswax candles and a reproducible Advent prayer sheet. We also offer *Advent wreaths—which are sold separately.*

Advent Candles and Wreaths are available NOW at

www.HolyHeroes.com/Advent

How to Use this Book

Hey, Mom and Dad ... and Kids, too!

We've put SPECIAL SYMBOLS throughout this book to help show you what to do during the day-to-day Jesse Tree activities.

HERE'S what they are and what they mean:

This means there's a **JESSE TREE of Salvation History VIDEO** to watch, too! *(You can purchase our Jesse Tree video in advance—it's reusable every year, and it has BONUS material, too!)*

READ FOR YOURSELF from the **BIBLE**. Next to this symbol you can find the Bible book, chapter, and verses listed for you to read for that day.

READ from THE PICTURE BIBLE —the BEST pre-teen Bible available! We'll tell you what pages to read so you don't get lost in the "Big Bible". *(Get your* ***Picture Bible*** *at* ***HolyHeroes.com!****)*

GET the ANSWER KEYS to all these JESSE TREE ACTIVITIES at

www.HolyHeroes.com/JesseTree

Now that you know what the SPECIAL SYMBOLS mean ...

Let your Advent journey to Christmas begin!

COME BACK to this page every **SUNDAY** in Advent to **COLOR** the correct **ADVENT CANDLE** below and **FILL IN** the correct **DATE**!

1st SUNDAY of Advent	2nd SUNDAY of Advent	3rd SUNDAY of Advent	4th SUNDAY of Advent
Date: ______________	Date: ______________	Date: ______________	Date: ______________

Have a Blessed ADVENT Season!

Day 1

The "Jesse Tree" of Salvation History

The Jesse Tree comes from what the prophet Isaiah said, **"There shall come forth a shoot from the stump of Jesse, and a branch shall grow out of his roots."** (Isaiah 11:1)

The Jesse Tree is a tree, (real or fake—**WATCH** the video to find out how to make one!) that ornaments are hung from. Each ornament represents a person who came before Jesus.

You can **READ Isaiah 11:1-5** for more prophesies about Jesus!

Where does the Jesse Tree start? ______________________

When does the Jesse Tree end? ______________________

We're so happy you've joined us for our journey through the JESSE TREE OF SALVATION HISTORY!

The Old Testament book of Isaiah and the Gospels of Matthew and Luke inspired the Jesse Tree. Isaiah was a man who prophesied the coming of the Messiah, and Matthew and Luke's Gospels deal with Jesus's family tree. This family tree—and all the people in it—reveal God's desire for the salvation of all people and the fulfillment of His promises.

Our journey will take us from the creation of the world to the Nativity of Our Lord. Are you ready?

WHAT IS SALVATION HISTORY?

Salvation History is the story of how God prepared the world for the birth of His Only Begotten Son, Jesus Christ! The Jesse Tree will introduce you to Old Testament figures who came before him. Throughout the Old Testament, people were eagerly waiting for our Savior to come...kind of like how you are waiting to open your presents on Christmas Day!

JESSE TREE ORNAMENTS

This book presents many day-by-day activities, for both older and younger kids, including making your own Jesse Tree ornaments for your home Jesse Tree! You can design your own ornaments or you can download, print off, and construct our designs for **FREE** available at **HolyHeroesJesseTree.com**!

HOLY HEROES JESSE TREE DVD

Get the DVD with all the Jesse Tree videos on it—**plus bonus videos**—that can be used over and over for every Advent.

This DVD is **ON SALE** now at **HolyHeroesJesseTree.com**!

Download all the ornaments and print them out at 3" diameter size (or larger).

READ the **Picture Bible** pages 491–492.

CONNECT the DOTS to complete the picture of a **JESSE TREE** with the ornaments on it and **COLOR** them.

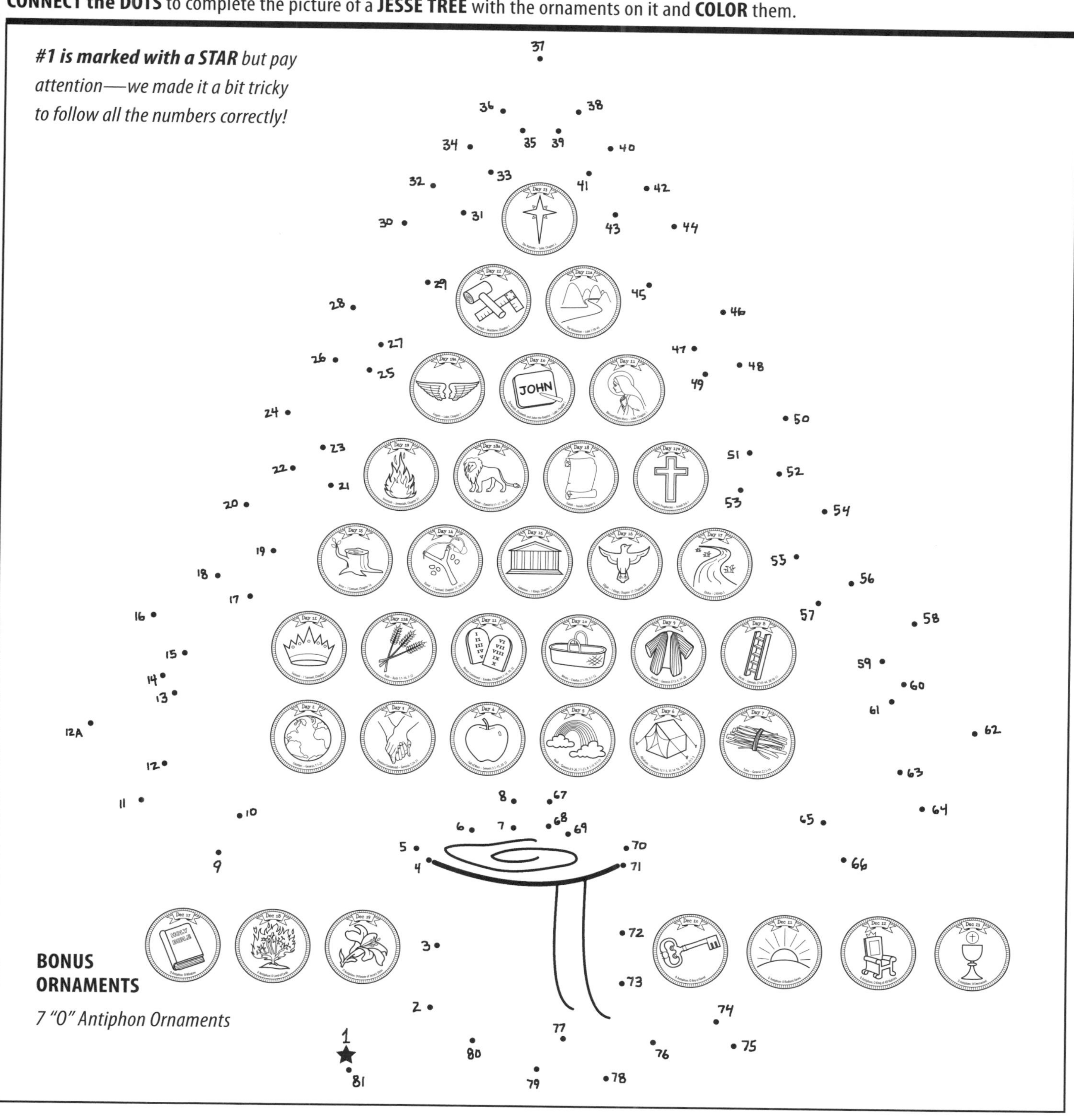

Day 2
CREATION for Beginners!

Today is our first day learning about Salvation History. Remember, Salvation History is God's plan from the very beginning to make it possible for you, your family, and everyone else, to come live with Him forever in Heaven!

First, God had to make the earth and everything we need to live on it. **Genesis 1:1-23** tells the story of how God created the world!

Reading the Bible

Do you know how to find readings from the Bible? We'll talk about them a lot, and you might want to read them for yourself. Let's use "Genesis 1:1-23" as an example on how to find Scripture readings.

The Bible is divided into big sections called Books. You start with the name of the Book in the Bible, in this case, "Genesis." The numbers are more complicated. "1:1-23" means chapter 1, verses 1 through 23. The first number, 1, is the chapter, which is a smaller part of each Biblical Book. Chapters are chunks of writing. The next numbers, "1-23", are the verse numbers. So, to read Genesis 1:1-23, you'd go to chapter 1 in the Book of Genesis and read the numbered sentences that go from 1 to 23.

FILL IN THE BLANKS below, using the pictures to help you. You can **COLOR** the pictures, too!

Sk+

DAY 1: God said, "Let there ________ __________. DAY 2: God created ___________ and ___________.

DAY 3: God created ___________ and ___________ and __________ and ___________.

Sk+

DAY 4: God created ___________ , ___________ and ___________ . DAY 5: God filled the ___________

with ___________ and the ___________ with __________ ___________.

TRICKY BONUS QUESTION

What Day did God Create these?

DAY ________

(find out tomorrow)

READ the **Picture Bible** pages 13–15.

COLOR in the pictures below. Then **FILL IN** the **BLANKS** and tell us the **DAY** that God made it first!

This is a ________________ in the sky.

God made the sky on the ________________ day.

This is ____.

God made "time" in the sky on the ________________ day.

These are __________ that live in the ______________. God filled the sky and sea with living creatures on the ____________ day.

Day 3

CREATION—Part 2

Now it's time to learn about what God did on the last 2 days of Creation.

You can **READ Genesis 1:24-31** through **Genesis 2:1-3.** Remember how to find these verses in the Bible? They start in the Book of Genesis, chapter 1, verses 24 through 31. Pay attention, this part is important! It's when God created the first man!

DECODE the Bible verse below to find out what God told them?
Write the missing words on the lines provided. *(Hint: The verse is from Genesis 1: 28.)*

2 x 2 = 2 x 4 =
2 x 3 = 2 x 5 =

God blessed them and said, " _____ ________ful and ___________ ,

$\frac{1}{2}$

fill the _______ and _______ due it, and _______ ________ inion

A B C

over the _______ of the _______ , and the _______ of the _______ ,

and over every living _________ .

READ the **Picture Bible** pages 16–18.

CONNECT the DOTS to complete the picture of some of the animals God created, then **COLOR** them.

Day 4
The Fall of Man

Today in the Jesse Tree video we learn about the first sin (Original Sin), which we call the Fall of Man. But not everything about the Fall was bad. It brought something wonderful, and you'll hear all about it in today's video.

Genesis 3:15 contains a promise called "The Protoevangelium," which is Latin for "First Gospel." It is the first time God tells us that Jesus Christ will come to save us from the effects of Adam's sin! Although God punishes Adam and Eve for their disobedience, God also promises to send a savior to "crush the head" of the serpent! In Genesis 3:15, God says He will send this savior through a woman who will have a son. The serpent will hate the woman and the son, but he will not be able to defeat them. This promise to send a savior is the Protoevangelium.

The sentences below reveal facts about the Fall of Man, but one word in each sentence is scrambled up. **UNSCRAMBLE** them and put the correct letters in the boxes to the right. Put a letter in each box. The letters in the gray boxes will help you answer the question at the very bottom!

1. Adam and Eve ate the forbidden **TRUFI**.
2. God said: "Do not eat the fruit of the knowledge of good and **LEVI**."
3. Adam and Eve lived in the **NAGRED** of Eden.
4. Eve said: "The **PRESENT** tricked me, and I ate."
5. Eve took the first **ITEB**.
6. The first book of the Bible is **SINEGES**.
7. Adam said: "The **MOWAN** gave me the fruit, and I ate."
8. God put a flaming **DROWS** by the tree of knowledge.
9. Traditionally we think the forbidden fruit was a **PLEAP**.
10. **MEBURICH** now guard Eden.
11. The Fall of Man is in the first book of the **BEBLI**.

To answer the question below, you can read DOWN the letters you put into the gray boxes:

In Genesis 3:15, God promised to send a Savior to save us from the effects of Adam's sin.

This is called **"The Protoevangelium,"** which is Latin for "___ ___ ___ ___ ___ ___ ___ ___ ___ ___ ___."

READ the **Picture Bible** pages 19–21.

OOPS! We forgot to identify who said or did each item below from Genesis, chapter 3!
CIRCLE who said or did each one in the last column—then you'll know the story of the Protoevangelium!

Quote	Who said or did this?
"You may eat of all the trees in the Garden, except the tree of the knowledge of good and evil, or you shall die."	Serpent Adam Eve God
"Did God say, 'You shall not eat of any tree of the garden?'"	Serpent Adam Eve God
"You shall not die."	Serpent Adam Eve God
Ate the first bite of the forbidden fruit.	Serpent Adam Eve God
"Have you eaten of the tree of which I commanded you not to eat?"	Serpent Adam Eve God
"The woman gave me the fruit, and I ate."	Serpent Adam Eve God
"The serpent tricked me, and I ate."	Serpent Adam Eve God
"I will put enmity between you and the woman, and between your seed and her seed; He shall bruise your head and you shall bruise His heel."	Serpent Adam Eve God

Day 5

NOAH in Salvation History

Today, we learn about Noah. This was a fun video for the Adventure Guides to make, and we think you'll really like it, too!

You can **READ** the story of Noah in **Genesis 6:5-20, 7:1-23, 8:1-17,** and **9:1-13.**

Many things in the story of Noah will remind you of the story of Adam and Eve. Some events are similar, and some are different. God makes promises to Noah's family just like He did to Adam and Eve. After all, when God floods the earth, only Noah's family is left alive. They're like new Adams and Eves. With God's help, they're able to thrive!

CIRCLE the smiley face in the following chart if the event was a good thing that happened in the stories of Adam and Eve or of Noah and his family. Circle the sad face if it was a bad thing that happened in the stories. If it did NOT happen to them, cross out both faces!

Event	Adam & Eve		Noah & His Family	
God had them take care of the animals	☺	☹	☺	☹
God gave them a family to be with them and help them	☺	☹	☺	☹
God blessed them	☺	☹	☺	☹
God told them to be fruitful and multiply and fill the earth	☺	☹	☺	☹
They obeyed God	☺	☹	☺	☹
They disobeyed God	☺	☹	☺	☹
They had to leave their home because of sinful actions	☺	☹	☺	☹
God promised a savior would come	☺	☹	☺	☹
God gave them a new place to live	☺	☹	☺	☹

A Helpful Hint: *Some events happened to BOTH of them!*

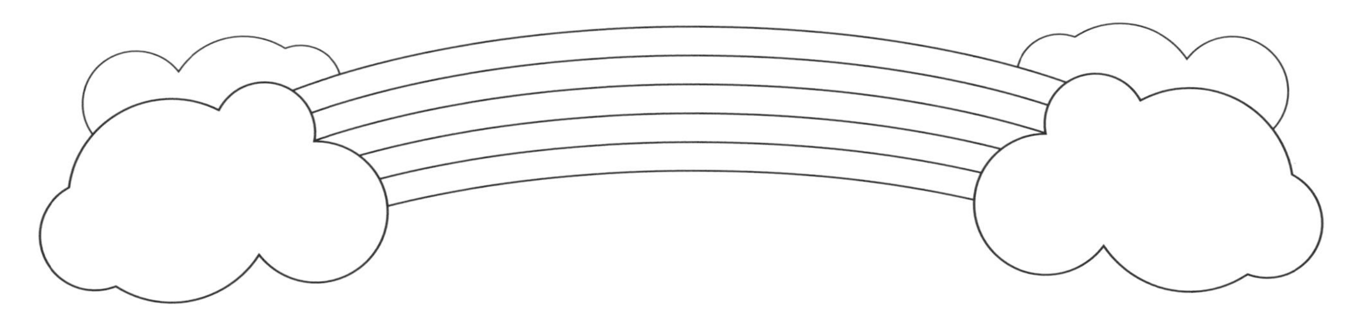

God gave Noah and his family a new home and a **sign** of His covenant never again to send a flood to destroy the earth (Genesis 9:11). What was the sign of this covenant? ______________________________

READ the **Picture Bible** pages 28–36. **COLOR** the picture of the ark in the stormy sky and floodwaters from the story of Noah.

Today's **WORD SEARCH** below is jam-packed with words that remind us about Noah. Can you **FIND** them all and **TELL** your mom & dad what all the words remind us about? (*If you don't understand what all the words mean—don't worry—ask your mom and dad!*)

M	K	G	N	L	N	W	A	T	E	R	N
K	J	M	W	E	S	R	O	H	A	I	G
Q	A	O	O	N	V	R	F	B	A	I	M
W	P	L	C	H	O	A	B	R	P	R	K
E	H	I	Y	D	E	I	R	N	A	Q	H
V	E	V	F	L	T	E	L	I	H	P	R
O	T	E	H	O	G	E	N	E	S	I	S
D	H	A	A	I	R	B	L	H	P	F	C
N	O	A	T	R	O	T	E	W	U	L	N
N	M	G	M	W	K	M	Y	Z	P	O	O
N	T	N	A	N	E	V	O	C	P	O	W
A	N	I	M	A	L	C	C	F	Y	D	T

WORDS TO FIND

Animal	Lion
Ark	Noah
Covenant	Olive
Cow	Pig
Dove	Puppy
Flood	Rabbit
Forty	Rain
Genesis	Rainbow
Ham	Raven
Horse	Shem
Japheth	Tiger
Leaf	Water

Words can go horizontally, vertically, and diagonally in all eight directions.

Day 6

ABRAHAM and the Promises of God

Abraham is an interesting figure in the Old Testament because we don't really know about his early life. We do know that he was a righteous and holy man. God told Abraham to leave his home and travel to a far away land. It must have been scary, but Abraham obeyed God—and God rewarded Abraham by fulfilling **THREE PROMISES**.

READ about Abraham in **Genesis 12:1-5, 13:14-16, 18:1-10**, and **21:1-3**.

What were the three promises God made to Abraham? You'll have to **"DECODE"** them by solving the **cryptogram** below! A cryptogram is a code in which each letter actually stands for another letter. Use the chart below to help you decode—we've filled in some of it for you!

Real letter:	A	B	C	D	E	F	G	H	I	J	K	L	M	N	O	P	Q	R	S	T	U	V	W	X	Y	Z
Code letter:					L								T		S											

Promise #1

"_ __LL ___E ___ _ __E__ N____N."

"O BOTT YRDL NKP R XILRM SRMOKS."

Promise #2

"_ __LL ___E ____ N__E __E__."

"O BOTT YRDL NKPI SRYL XILRM."

Meaning: *you will have lots of descendants*

Promise #3

"_ __LL ___E ___ _ _LE___N_ __ _LL __E ____L_E_ __ __E E____."

"O BOTT YRDL NKP R ZTLJJOSX MK RTT MVL URYOTOLJ KU MVL LRIMV."

God also changed Abram's name to what? *(see Genesis 17:4-5)*

____

RZIRVRY

God changed Abram's wife's name from Sarai to what? *(see Genesis 17:15-16)*

_____

JRIRV

READ the **Picture Bible** pages 38–50.

THINK about the Bible story, then **ANSWER** the following questions.

1. Who was Abraham's wife?
   a. Hannah
   b. Sarah
   c. Mary
   d. Rachel

2. Who was Abraham's son?
   a. Isaac
   b. David
   c. Jacob
   d. Israel

3. Who did God tell Abraham to sacrifice to him?
   a. His wife
   b. His brother
   c. His son
   d. His friend

4. What did God promise Abraham?
   a. He would let him live a long time
   b. He would send angels to help him
   c. He would be the father of many descendants
   d. He would have a happy marriage

COLOR the picture of Abraham and his beloved son, Isaac.

Day 7
ISAAC, Abraham's Son

Isaac was the fulfillment one of God's promises. But God still had another test of faith for Abraham.

LEARN about it by **READING Genesis 22:1-14.** Abraham is called "Our Father in Faith" because he was obedient even when it was very hard. He trusted God even when he couldn't see what God's plan was!

THINK about the story, then **ANSWER** the following questions. We've put in some pictures as hints!

Abraham trusted God and obeyed Him. But—who else in this story was obedient and trusting? *(Hint: he carried the wood up the mountain!)* ____________________

Who else in the story has only one son? *(Hint: Remember John 3:16)* ____________________

What did God's only Son carry up a hill?

____

Whom does God send to speak to Abraham? ____________________

What does Abraham sacrifice in place of his son? ____________________

READ the **Picture Bible** pages 51–66. **CONNECT the DOTS** in the picture below.

Isaac had to show his obedience to God, Our Father in Heaven, by obeying Abraham, the father God had especially chosen for Isaac on earth. This reminds us of what Jesus says in the **Gospel of Matthew** about His Father.

Can you **CRACK** the **CRYPTOGRAM** below to decode and read what the Gospel said? We've filled in some words for you to get started!

NOT EVERYONE ___ ____ __ __, '_____, _____,' **SHALL** _____ ___ ________

CNE RSRQXNCR GJN IUXI EN YR, 'PNQA, PNQA,' IJUPP RCERQ EJR LZCHANY

__ ______, ___ __ ___ ____ ___ ____ __ __ **FATHER** ___ __ __ ______.

NM JRUSRC, VTE JR GJN ANRI EJR GZPP NM YX MUEJRQ GJN ZI ZC JRUSRC.

(MATTHEW CHAPTER _____, **VERSE** _______-___)

(YUEEJRG WJUDERQ IRSRC, SRQIR EGRCEX - NCR)

Day 8
JACOB in Salvation History

Isaac was an obedient son . . . but his son, Jacob, was not! Jacob tricked his father to steal his brother's blessing, and that led to a lot of problems for his whole family. Jacob even had to run away so he wouldn't get killed!

You can **READ** about it in **Genesis 27 and 28**.

To help you with **TODAY'S PUZZLE**, we have provided a **WORD BANK**. You can find the answers that fit the crossword in the word bank.
BE CAREFUL: some of the words in the bank will NOT be used in the puzzle—we didn't want to make it too easy!

DOWN

2 He became blind in his old age.
3 A blessing derives its meaning and effectiveness from the ______ of the word of God, the first part of a blessing.
4 By celebrating a blessing, we can _____ events in our lives.
7 A blessing is not a sacrament, but a _____.
8 When objects are blessed, we always have in mind the _____ who use them.
10 Stole his brother Esau's blessing.
11 A blessing has ____ parts.
13 The first blessing of God to Adam and Eve was to be _____ and multiply.
18 Jacob's _____, Rebecca, convinced him to trick his father.
19 In keeping with an ancient tradition, the tracing of the sign of the _____ often accompanies a blessing.

ACROSS

1 In most circumstances, if a _____ is present, he should preside over the blessing.
5 First part of a blessing is the proclamation of the _____ of God.
6 Second part of a blessing is _____ of God's goodness and petition for His help.
9 The person presiding in a blessing represents the ______.
12 There is a blessing for a Christmas _____ or Nativity Scene.
14 There is a blessing for an Advent ____.
15 After the ____ God blessed Noah and his family.
16 The story of Jacob and Esau is in this book of the Bible.
17 There is a blessing for a Christmas ____.
20 The source from which every good gift comes--including blessings!
21 A blessing is a ______ action of the Church. (Hint: we also talk about ____ colors!)
22 A sacramental prepares a person to receive _____ and to better cooperate with it.
23 Although a human being pronounces a blessing, it does not have a merely human _____.

WORD BANK:

Church, cross, flood, fruitful, Genesis, God, grace, Isaac, Jacob, liturgical, manger, mother, people, praise, priest, proclamation, sacramental, sanctify, source, tree, two, word, wreath, Xavier, yarn, Zechariah

READ the **Picture Bible** pages 72–82 and 93.

SOLVE the **3 MAZES** to answer the **3 QUESTIONS** about Jacob below!

*(Start at the **CENTER** of each maze and work outward to the correct answer!)*

1. Who does Jacob cheat out of his birthright?

a. Esau b. Isaac

2. Who does Jacob fight with in the night?

a. an angel b. Esau

3. What was Jacob's name changed to?

a. Laban b. Israel

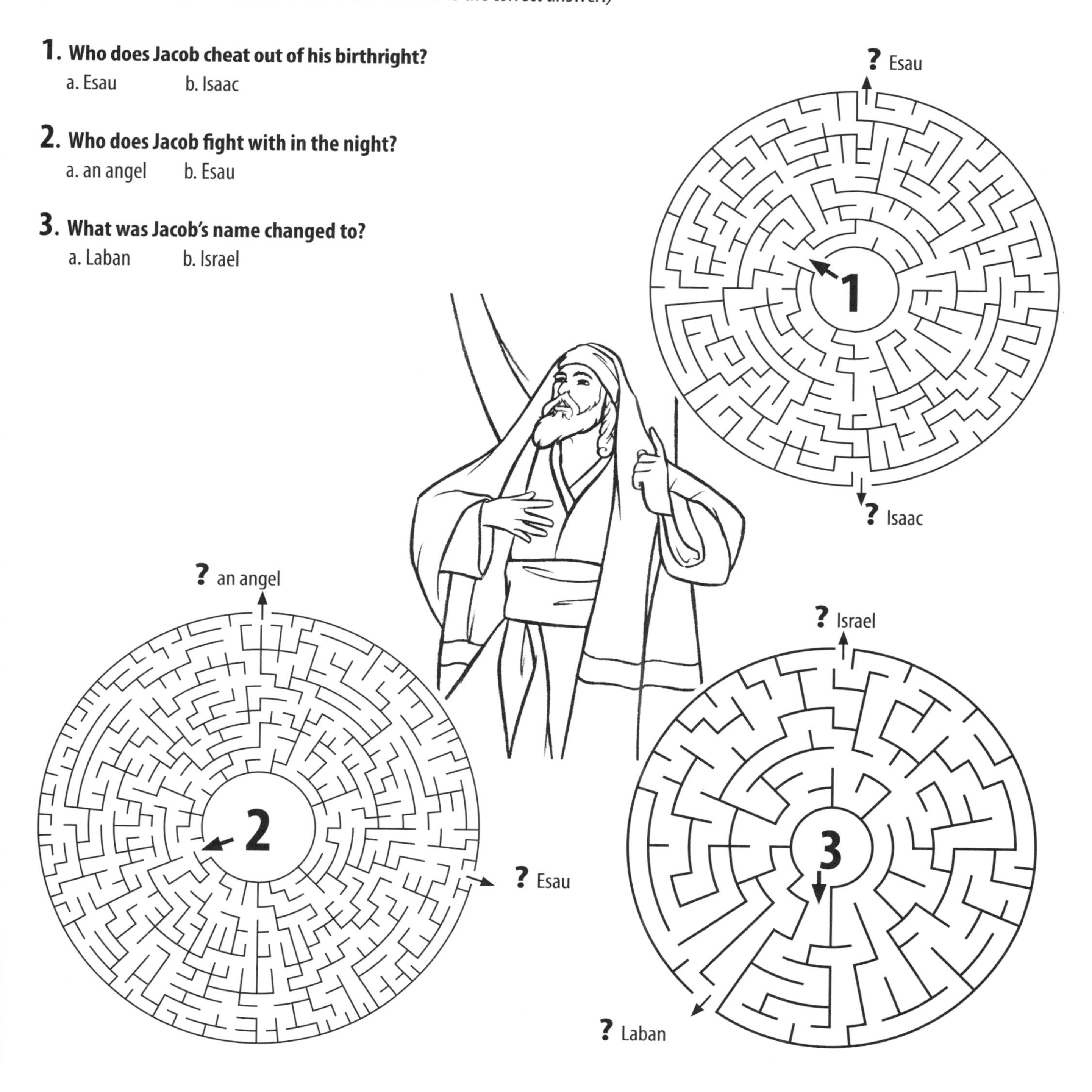

Day 9

JOSEPH, Son of Jacob, in Salvation History

Jacob tricked his father to steal from his brother... in the same way, Jacob's sons also tricked him to steal from their brother! But God's plans are never wrecked by the sins of people. **WATCH** our Jesse Tree VIDEO to learn more about it!

Below are pictures that should **REMIND YOU** of some of the characters in the Jesse Tree.

Next to each picture, **WRITE** down the name of the person and **why** the picture reminds you of him.
*(If you need help from Mom, Dad, or a sibling—just **ask**!)*

Tent reminds you of ...

____

Because he ...

____

____

____

Sticks remind you of ...

____

Because he ...

____

____

____

Ladder reminds you of ...

____

Because he ...

____

____

____

Coat reminds you of ...

____

Because he ...

____

____

____

READ the **Picture Bible** pages 94 and 97–122.

What did Joseph's brothers do to him? (Make your way through the **MAZE** below to find the right answer.)

START HERE ★

START at the ★ at the TOP and exit at the BOTTOM to find which is the CORRECT answer.

Licensed from **mazegenerator.net**

?↓ **Forgave him**

?↓ **Sold him into slavery**

?↓ **Complained to their father**

THINK back on this week, and **WRITE** down what you will do to be even more obedient to your parents and God—just like Isaac!

I will do these things:

Day 10

MOSES in Salvation History

Moses was a man who was very obedient to God, although he sometimes argued with God about His commands! He had one of the most exciting lives of anyone in the Old Testament—even his time as a baby was an adventure.

You can **READ** about Moses in **Exodus chapters 2-4.**

Moses was angry about something.
What was it?

SOLVE the maze to find out why Moses was angry. **Start at the center** and find your way out to the **CORRECT ANSWER.**

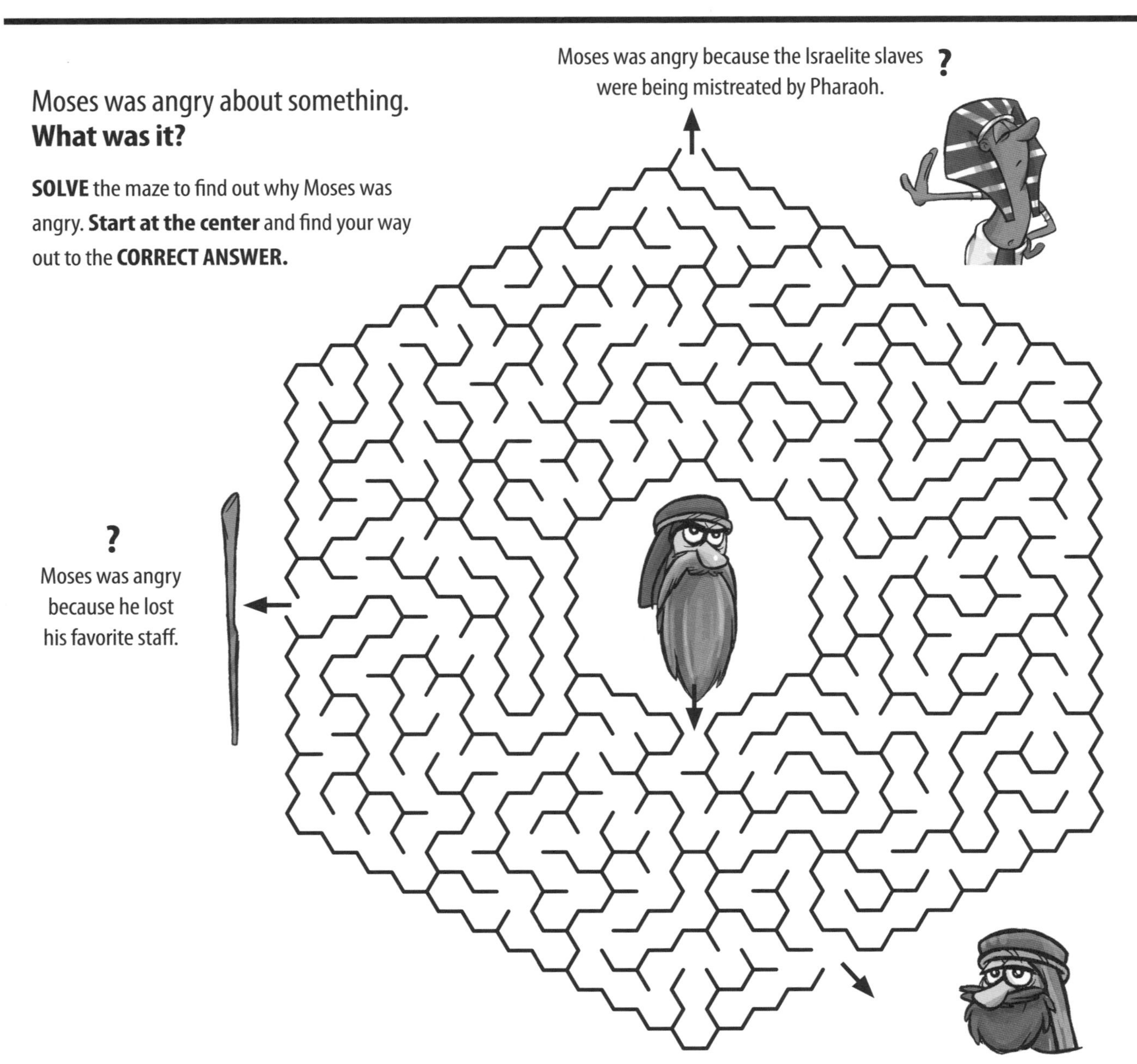

? Moses was angry because Aaron could sing better than he could.

READ the **Picture Bible** pages 125–135.

COLOR the picture of Moses and the burning bush above and **ANSWER** the questions below :

1. What did Moses' mother do with him when he was 3 months old? (Exodus 2:3)
   a. Handed him to Pharaoh
   b. Put him in a basket and placed it in the river Nile
   c. Let his big sister babysit him

2. Moses became angry about… (Exodus 2:11)
   a. The Israelites being mistreated as slaves to the Egyptians
   b. His boring life as a prince
   c. Pharaoh's outlandish clothes

3. What did Moses do when he ran away from Egypt? (Exodus 3:1)
   a. Built tents for desert people
   b. Managed palace construction
   c. Became a shepherd

4. What did God say to Moses from the burning bush? (Exodus 3:5)
   a. Take off your hat for this is holy ground
   b. Have a seat on this holy ground and listen
   c. Take off your shoes for this is holy ground

Day 11

More about MOSES in Salvation History

Today we continue learning about MOSES and his part in the plan of Salvation History! God sent Moses to lead the Exodus of the slaves out of Egypt, then He gave Moses the Ten Commandments on Mount Sinai.

You can **READ** about it in the book of **Exodus 7:14, 7:19,** and **7:31.**

COLOR the picture of Moses with the Ten Commandments.

UNSCRAMBLE the letters to spell out the **Ten Commandments**.

Behavior towards God

1. VEAH ON THOER DGOS EROFEB EM

____

2. OD TON ESUBA YM MEAN

____

3. PEEK HET BATHSAB LYOH

____

Behavior towards others

4. NOHOR RUYO THERFA NAD THERMO

____

5. OD TON LIKL

____

6. OD TON MITCOM TERYADUL

____

7. OD TON LEAST

____

8. OD TON ELI

____

9. OD TON TECOV NOTAHERS ESUOPS

____

10. OD TON TECOV NOTAHERS DOGOS

____

READ the **Picture Bible** pages 136–191.

Today's **WORD SEARCH** below is jam-packed with words that remind us about Moses.
Can you **FIND** them all and **TELL** your Mom & Dad what all the words remind us about?

M	Z	T	P	G	Y	E	L	I	A	H	R	S	W
C	O	M	M	A	N	D	M	E	N	T	S	E	D
S	J	I	K	X	J	S	P	N	M	L	A	S	R
T	N	F	S	S	F	H	L	O	Y	D	N	O	E
A	J	G	L	R	A	F	D	A	L	F	G	M	H
N	R	I	O	R	A	E	J	D	V	X	E	N	P
G	O	G	A	C	E	E	S	R	E	E	L	F	E
B	S	O	J	R	O	T	L	E	L	A	R	D	H
N	H	X	F	L	P	W	E	I	I	F	T	Y	S
A	P	L	A	G	U	E	S	K	T	L	T	H	T
A	S	S	E	N	K	R	A	D	S	E	F	R	G
R	R	Z	F	O	R	T	Y	Y	E	A	R	S	N
O	F	L	A	C	N	E	D	L	O	G	B	E	V
N	K	G	B	L	O	O	D	V	T	Y	T	M	N

WORDS TO FIND

Aaron
Angel
Basket
Blood
Boils
Commandments
Cows

Darkness
Death
Eygpt
Flies
Forty
years
Freedom

Frogs
Gnats
Golden
Calf
Hail
Israelite
Moses

Pharaoh
Plagues
Shepherd
Slavery
Ten

Words can go horizontally, vertically and diagonally in all eight directions.

Day 11a

RUTH in Salvation History

The Book of Ruth is one of the two books in the Bible named after a woman (the other one is Esther). This book is about the ties and the strength of family and how powerful it can be, even when you weren't born into the family, even when they are your in-laws. Ruth's story isn't about miracles and it isn't about deliverance; this story is about family, more specifically, the love of family. Ruth gave up everything to follow Naomi, her mother-in-law, even though she really didn't have to. She even said to Naomi, "Where you go I will go, and where you lodge I will lodge; your people shall be my people, and your God my God" (Ruth 1:16). It must have taken a lot of faith and love for her to say this. Because of Ruth's unconditional love for Naomi and her family, Ruth would become the great grandmother of David, from whom Jesus descended.

You can **READ** the whole story in the **Book of Ruth.** it's short!

HELP RUTH! Complete the **MAZE** below correctly so you can figure out the **TWO NAMES** needed below!

Ruth went to a town in Judah to get food.
Write the name of that town here:

____

A very famous person was born in that town.
Write the name of that person here:

____

Where should Ruth go?

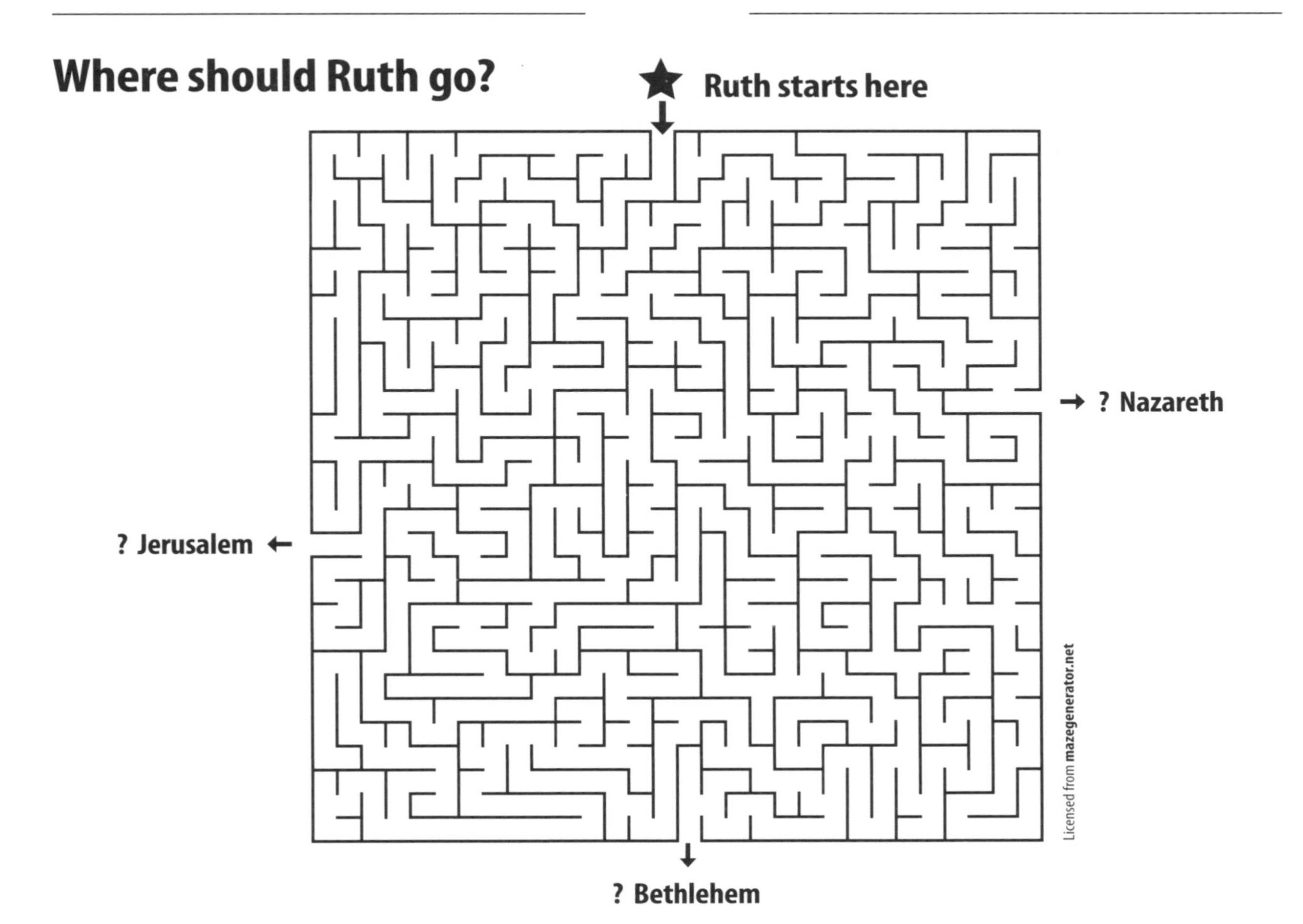

READ the **Picture Bible** pages 247–252.

UNSCRAMBLE the words in **BOLD** below. These words describe how Ruth, Naomi, and Boaz behaved. God took care of them all, rewarding them for these acts of love.

THILUFAF = They were all ____________________ towards God and each other.

Write down how you can show this trait towards your family this Advent: ____________________

____

____

SENSKNID = They all acted with ____________________ towards each other.

Write down how you can show this trait towards your family this Advent: ____________________

____

____

NEGESOUR = They all were ____________________ and shared what they had with each other.

Write down how you can show this trait towards your family this Advent: ____________________

____

____

THINK back on this week, and **WRITE** down some other ways to show love to your family.

I will do these things:

____________________ ____________________

____________________ ____________________

____________________ ____________________

____________________ ____________________

Day 11a

RUTH in Salvation History

COLOR the picture below of Ruth and Boaz at their wedding!

The Nativity Manger Scene

We created a fun Nativity Manger Scene activity to help your family celebrate the remainder of Advent!

DOWNLOAD your **Nativity Manger Scene** activity at: **www.HolyHeroes.com/Nativity**

We've made it easy for you to make your OWN manger scene. **Just follow the simple steps below**:

1. **Print off** colorable manger scene cutouts that you download.

2. **Color them, cut them out,** and **tape or glue** them onto some of **your own cardboard** so they are more sturdy *(paper plates work great in place of cardboard)*.

3. **Cut out** a bunch of your own **cardboard "stands"** and **insert** them **on the bottoms** so the cutouts can **stand up**.

4. **Set up the stable background** and **put the animals around** the stable. Don't forget to **color the little animals** that you will find hidden in the stable already!

REMEMBER: Some of the manger scene items are not to be used right now—save them for later when it gets closer to Christmas morning!

You can color them and get them ready now...but just wait a few more days before you use them. Okay?

Day 12

SAMUEL in Salvation History

Samuel is a very important person in Salvation History because he anointed the first and second kings of Israel. God began speaking to Samuel when he was young, then He kept giving Samuel very important tasks to do.

You can **READ** about it in **1 Samuel chapter 3**.

God began speaking to Samuel when he was young, then He kept giving Samuel very important tasks to do.

HELP Samuel do what God tells him to do! Figure out which letters you need to find the answer to the final question.

FIRST, answer the questions below—the letters are jumbled.

What did Eli tell Samuel to reply to God when He calls?

_(3) _(5) _ _   _ _ _ _, for _ _(9) _   _ _(13) _ _ _ _ _(8)   _(12) _ _ _ _(4)

KEAPS   RDOL   YTH   VANTSER   REAHS

God told Samuel to anoint Saul as the first what?

_ _ _ _ of _ _ _ _ _(2) _(10)

NGKI   REALSI

Saul lost the kingship because He did what?

_ _ _ _ _(6) _(7) _ _(11) _   _ _ _

DSBYDIOEE   GDO

NEXT, find the correct path through the **MAZE** on the right to answer the question, and write the answer below.

? Naphtali

Samuel STARTS HERE

? Benjamin

? Issachar

What tribe of Israel did Saul belong to? _ _ _ _(1) _ _(14) _ _

Samuel was told by God to anoint a new king of Israel.

TELL SAMUEL where God wants him to go by filling in the answer here, inserting the numbered letters from the questions above.

_ _ _ _ _ in _ _ _ _ _ _ _ _ _

1 2 3 4 5   6 7 8 9 10 11 12 13 14

READ the **Picture Bible** pages 253–274. **COLOR** the picture of Eli telling Hannah that God will answer her prayers.

Day 13

JESSE in Salvation History

Today we learn about JESSE, for whom the "Jesse Tree" is named. Jesse is the great-great (that's 24 "greats"!) grandfather of Jesus.

What was the name of the son of Jesse whom Samuel anointed to be the next king? ____________

You can **READ** about it in **1 Samuel 16:1-13.**

CRACK the CODE to find out which son of Jesse God asked Samuel to anoint as the new King of Israel!

Real letter:	A	B	C	D	E	F	G	H	I	J	K	L	M	N	O	P	Q	R	S	T
Code letter:	1	2	3	4	5	6	7	8	9	10	11	12	13	14	15	16	17	18	19	20

Real letter:	U	V	W	X	Y	Z
Code letter:	21	22	23	24	25	26

God told Samuel to go to ____________ to the home of ____________.
2-5-20-8-12-5-8-5-13 **10-5-19-19-5**

God said, "You shall ____________ one of his sons which I name to you as the next King."
1-14-15-9-14-20

Jesse brought out ____________ of his sons, but God did not choose any of them.
19-5-22-5-14

Jesse's youngest son was in the ____________ tending the ____________.
6-9-5-12-4 **19-8-5-5-16**.

"Fetch him," said Samuel. When he appeared, God said, "____________ him, for this is he."
1-14-15-9-14-20

The boy's name was ____________.
4-1-22-9-4.

Jesse was the great-great-great-great [24 'greats'] grandfather of ____________.
10-5-19-21-19

READ the **Picture Bible** pages 275–280.

VESPERS and the MAGNIFICAT

During the 2nd Joyful Mystery, the Blessed Virgin Mary says a prayer thanking God for blessing her. **The Magnificat** is a very famous prayer that is sometimes called "The Canticle of Mary" *(canticle means "song")*, and it is prayed during **VESPERS** every evening. Vespers is a special time where people, often religious orders like monks and priests, get together and pray at the end of the day.

You can **READ** the prayer in **Luke 1:46-55**.

HELP the **Adventure Guides** get to where they can pray **Vespers**!

Day 14

DAVID in Salvation History

You've heard Jesus called the "Son of David," haven't you? **Well, today we learn about David!**—and there is a lot about David in the Bible!

READ some exciting stories about David as a young boy in **1 Samuel chapters 16-17**.

COLOR the picture of David as a young shepherd and **ANSWER** the questions below—color the harp, crown, slingshot and five smooth stones, too!

Why is a harp pictured near David?

____

Why is a crown also pictured?

____

Why is a slingshot with 5 smooth stones also pictured?

____

Who did David say would deliver Goliath into his hands?

____

READ the **Picture Bible** pages 281–362. **CONNECT** the DOTS below to complete the picture.

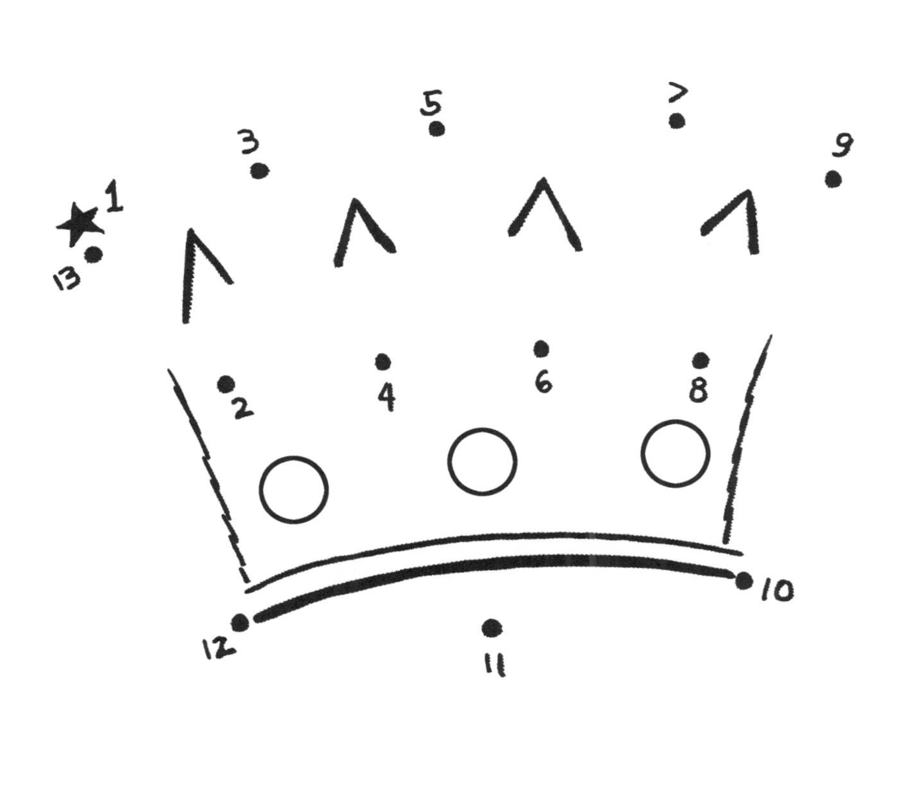

ANSWER the questions below about David.

1. David is whose ancestor? *(Hint: There is more than one right answer!)*
   a. Joseph
   b. Mary
   c. Jesus
   d. Ruth

2. David became the king of ____________?
   a. Israel
   b. Jerusalem
   c. Bethlehem
   d. Persia

3. David wanted to build what for God?
   a. A castle
   b. A temple
   c. A larger tent
   d. A kingdom

4. What did God tell him to do?
   a. To go right ahead
   b. To wait a few years
   c. To have his son do that, not him
   d. To first start a war

Day 15
SOLOMON in Salvation History

Solomon was the son of King David and when he became king after his father died, God gave him the gift of great wisdom.

READ about Solomon in **1 Kings chapter 3**.

SOLVE the **CRYPTOGRAM** to answer the **6 QUESTIONS** below.
(We filled in all the letters in the word "SOLOMON" to help you

Real letter:	A	B	C	D	E	F	G	H	I	J	K	L	M	N	O	P	Q	R	S	T	U	V	W	X	Y	Z
Code letter:												N	O	P	Q				U							

Where did Solomon go to pray to God? _ _ _ _ _ _
I K D G Q P

Who spoke to Solomon in a dream? _ _ _
I Q F

What did Solomon ask for? _ _ _ _ _ _
Y K U F Q O

What did he NOT ask for? _ _ _ _ _ _ _ _ **and** _ _ _ _ _ _
(Hint: See 1 Kings 3:11) N Q P I N K H G T K E J G U

What did Solomon build for God? _ _ _ _ _ _ _
C V G O R N G

How long did the temple take to be built? _ _ _ _ _ **years**
U G X G P

READ the **Picture Bible** pages 363–379.

The Ark of the Covenant was inside the Holy of Holies in the Temple.

Inside the Ark was a golden pot of manna and what TWO other items?

ENTER the Ark of the Covenant and make your way to the **TWO ROOMS** that contain the other two items.

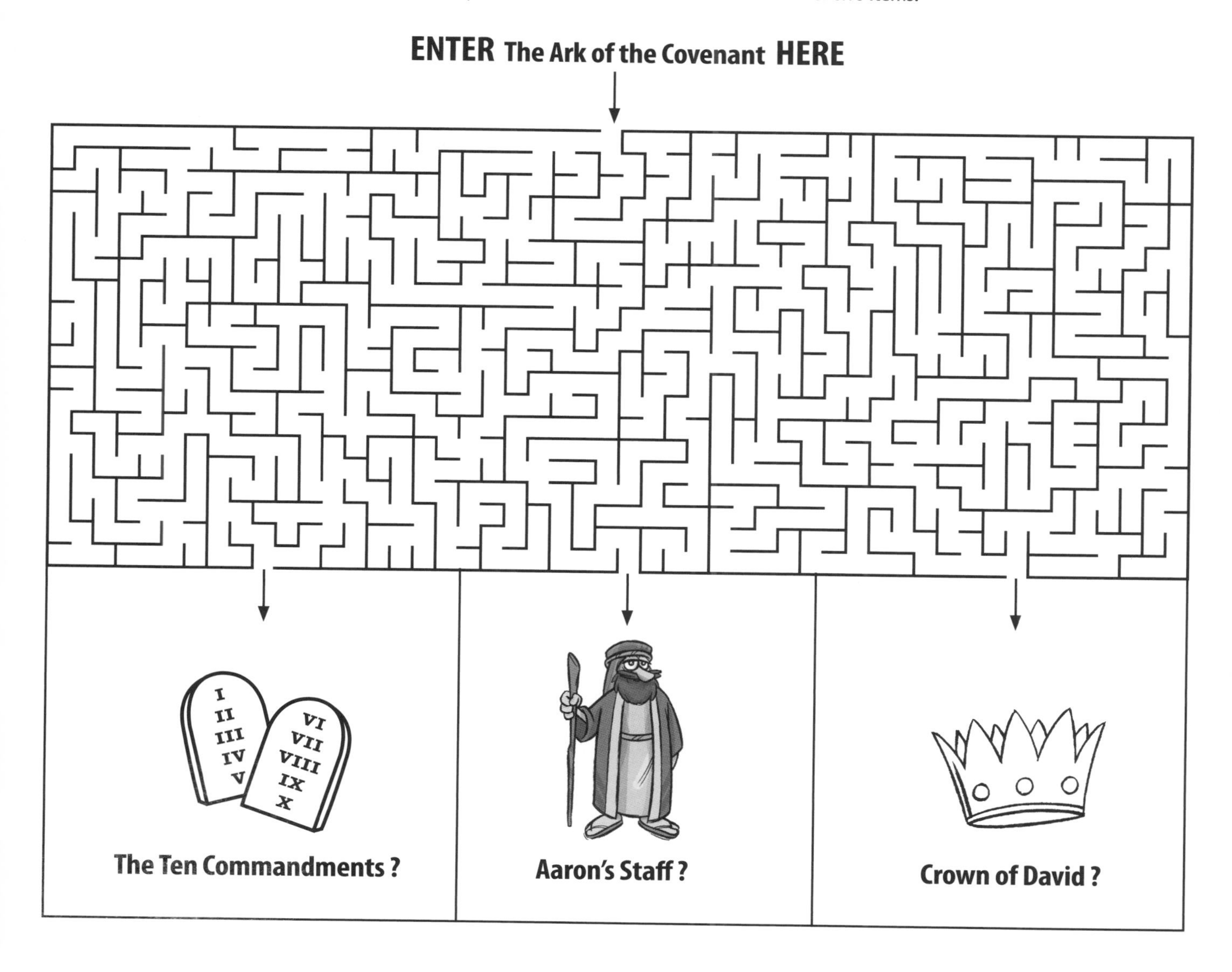

If you want to know more about what was inside the Ark of the Covenant and why *(and what it means to us as Catholics today!)*, you can get our VIDEO DVD **"Holy Heroes: Inside the Sacraments—The Holy Eucharist"** which explains all about it in a way even children can understand!

Day 16

ELIJAH in Salvation History

Elijah was a great prophet during a time when many people were worshipping false gods. The people simply did not have faith that the One True God would fulfill His promises to their ancestors and continue to care for them. However, Elijah trusted God, so God sent him as a messenger and used him to perform many miracles.

READ about Elijah in **1 Kings chapters 17 and 18**.

God has done many wonderful things to take care of you, too. But sometimes we start thinking of the things we wish we had, instead of being grateful for what we have been given! It is especially difficult to be thankful when there are lots of bad things around us; it was the same during Elijah's time, when a long famine struck. Everyone was hungry, and many people thought they would die!

We should always be grateful and thank the people who help us to live and become holy. This pleases God very much. It is especially important during Christmas time that we tell God how thankful we are for what we have, instead of telling Him we'll only be thankful if we get certain Christmas presents!

WRITE down some things that you are **thankful for**—then thank the person who made it possible!

This Advent, I am especially thankful to God for:

____

____

____

I am thankful to my parents for:

____

____

____

I am thankful to my friends and siblings for:

____

____

____

____

READ the **Picture Bible** pages 384–409.

Elijah saw God perform many miracles to try to teach the people not to worship false gods, but instead to worship the One True God! God did many magnificent miracles to show them His Power. One time, God told Elijah to go to Mount Horeb and wait inside a cave. God said He would pass by the entrance of the cave, and when Elijah heard Him pass by, he was to go outside the cave to speak with God.

Help Elijah know when he should leave the cave.

Outside the cave, Elijah heard a strong wind, an earthquake, a fire, and a small voice. Which one signals that God is passing by?
The **ANSWER** to the maze will tell you!

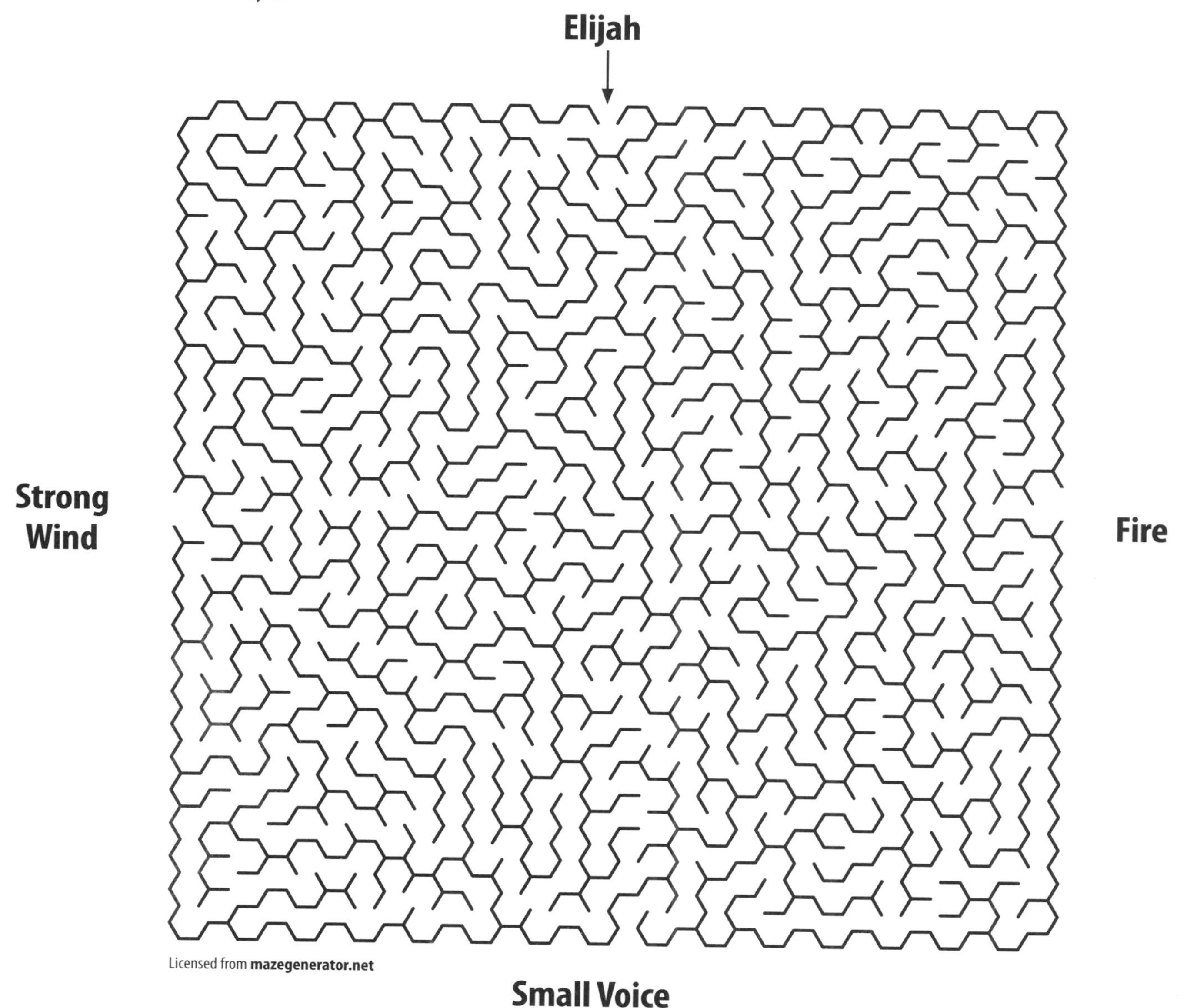

Day 17

ELISHA in Salvation History

Elisha was a disciple of Elijah (don't get their names confused!), and he became a great prophet after him. Just like Elijah, God performed many miracles through Elisha. Today's Jesse Tree VIDEO tells about one of them!

READ about Elisha in **2 Kings chapter 5**.

WRITE the name of the person that each illustration reminds you of and why on the lines below. **COLOR** the illustrations then draw a line from each illustration to the name of the person it reminds you of. Explain to your Mom & Dad what they all mean!

The Slingshot reminds me of ...

____

Because he ...

____

____

I II III IV V VI VII VIII IX X

The Crown reminds me of ...

____

Because he ...

____

____

The Temple reminds me of ...

____

Because he ...

____

____

Stone Tablets remind me of ...

____

Because he ...

____

____

The Stump reminds me of ...

____

Because he ...

____

____

The Wheat reminds me of ...

____

Because she ...

____

____

READ the **Picture Bible** pages 384 and 410–435.

ELISHA anointed a King of Israel, but we forgot his name: **What was the new King's name?** ______________________________

MAKE your way through the **MAZE** below to find the correct answer. Then you can **COLOR** the picture at the bottom.

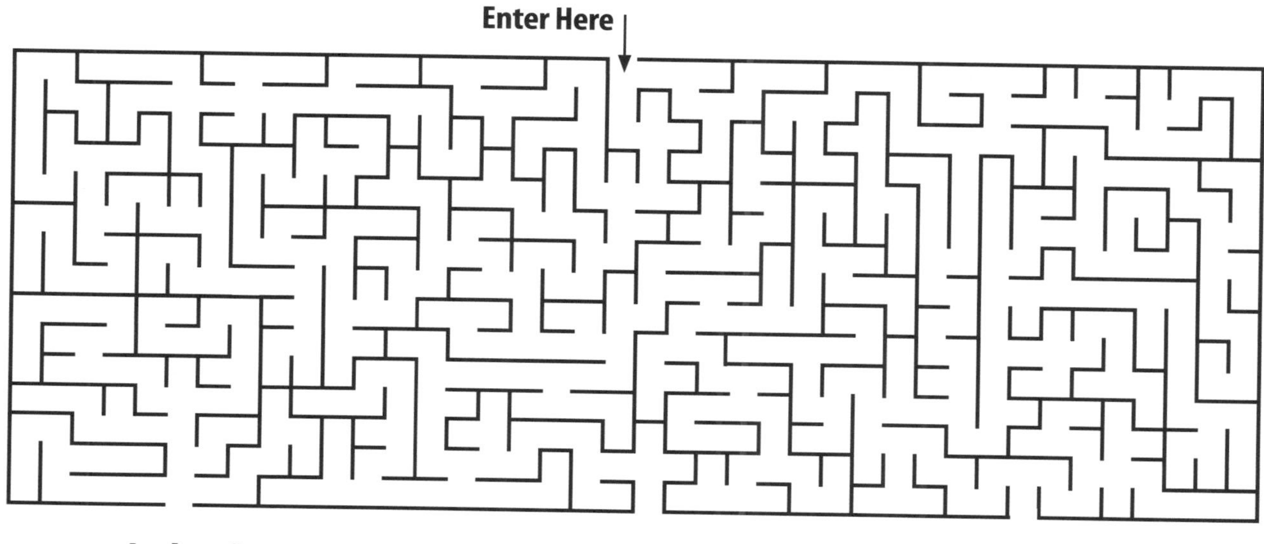

Joshua? **Jehu?** **Josiah?**

Day 17a

ISAIAH'S Prophecies about the Messiah

Today's video is about Isaiah's prophecy about the coming Messiah, Jesus Christ! Isaiah even foretold how the Messiah would save us from our sins!

READ about it in **Isaiah 9:6-7** and **53:5**.

What did Isaiah prophesy? Use the chart below to crack the code to find out!

Here's how: Find the letter to put in each blank in the questions below by following the first symbol **across** and the second symbol **up** in the chart.

For example:

△>

is the letter M.

○	A	B	C	D	E
□	F	G	H	I	J
△	K	L	M	N	O
●	P	Q	R	S	T
◇	U	V	W	Y	Z
	∞	Ω	>	<	=

1. What is one of the names the Messiah will be called?

___ ___ ___ ___ ___ ___   ___ ___ ___

△> □< □Ω □> ●= ◇<   □Ω △= ○<

(Wow! This means the Messiah will be more than just a man!)

2. What throne will the Messiah be given?

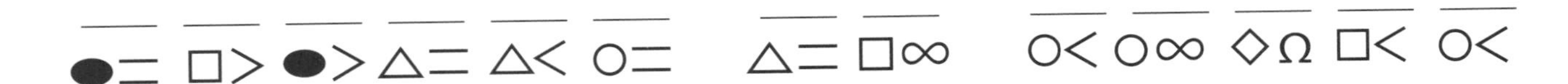

(This means that the Messiah will rule over all Israel!)

3. When did Isaiah prophesy the Messiah's kingdom would end?

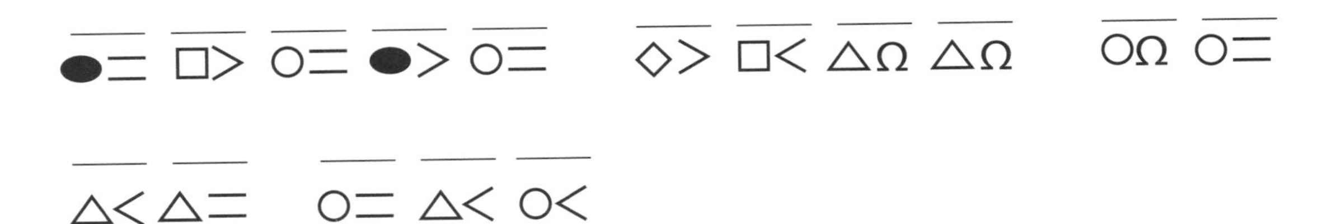

READ the **Picture Bible** page 492.

Isaiah prophesied when, where, and how the Messiah would come! **COLOR** the picture of Jesus' birth below.

Day 18
ISAIAH in Salvation History

God sent many prophets to Israel. They told the people to stop sinning and to repent. Then God sent Isaiah, the prophet who would tell them what the promised Messiah would be like.

READ about it in **Isaiah chapter 6.**

After you've watched the video, take this **QUIZ** about Isaiah!

1. The Book of Isaiah is the longest in the bible.
   a. True
   b. False

2. Isaiah is quoted how many times in the bible?
   a. Once
   b. More than fifty
   c. Fifteen
   d. Never

3. There are 66 chapters in the Book of Isaiah.
   a. True
   b. False

4. What is Isaiah sometimes called?
   a. The Prophet of Doom
   b. The Messianic Prophet
   c. The People's Prophet
   d. A man crying out in the Desert

5. The Book of Isaiah is sometimes split into two books called First Isaiah and Second Isaiah.
   a. True
   b. False

6. Isaiah foretold the coming of Christ.
   a. True
   b. False

SOLVE the **CRYPTOGRAM** below to reveal what Isaiah heard the seraphim say. Isaiah gave us the "O Antiphons" which tell us about God, so we've filled in the "O's" and the words referring to God for you already! *(If you're stumped, go to Isaiah 6:3.)*

Real letter:	A	B	C	D	E	F	G	H	I	J	K	L	M	N	O	P	Q	R	S	T	U	V	W	X	Y	Z
Code letter:				R				Z	B			M			K			H	Q							

```
_O__, _O__, _O__, __ ___ LORD O_ _O___;
ZKMG, ZKMG, ZKMG, BQ JZF MKHR KN ZKQJQ;

___ __O__ _____ __ ____ O_ HIS __O__.
JZF SZKMF FIHJZ BQ NDMM KN ZBQ CMKHG.
```

Where have you heard something very much like this? ________________________________

READ the **Picture Bible** pages 491–492.

Once, **ISAIAH** saw a vision of God sitting on His throne and six-winged seraphim were with Him.

Day 18a

DANIEL in Salvation History

The prophet Daniel lived during a time when the Jews were not allowed to live in Israel. He became an adviser to the Persian king, but the other advisers to the king became very jealous of him—and they plotted against him.

READ about it in the **Book of Daniel, chapter 6.**

WATCH the video and then **ANSWER** the questions below.

1. Where did Daniel live?
   a. Persia
   b. Israel
   c. Asia
   d. Babylon

2. The names of Daniel's three friends were . . .
   a. Nebuchadnezzar, Cyrus, and Saul
   b. Lucy, Susan, and Peter
   c. Shadrach, Meshach, and Abednego
   d. Aragorn, Legolas, and Gimli

3. Daniel could interpret what?
   a. Stories
   b. Messages
   c. Dreams
   d. Visions

4. Why was Daniel thrown in the lions' den?
   a. He was mean
   b. The king didn't like him
   c. The wise men were jealous
   d. The lions were hungry

HELP Daniel and his friends get safely to Babylon ... **START** at the **STAR** and exit at the bottom.

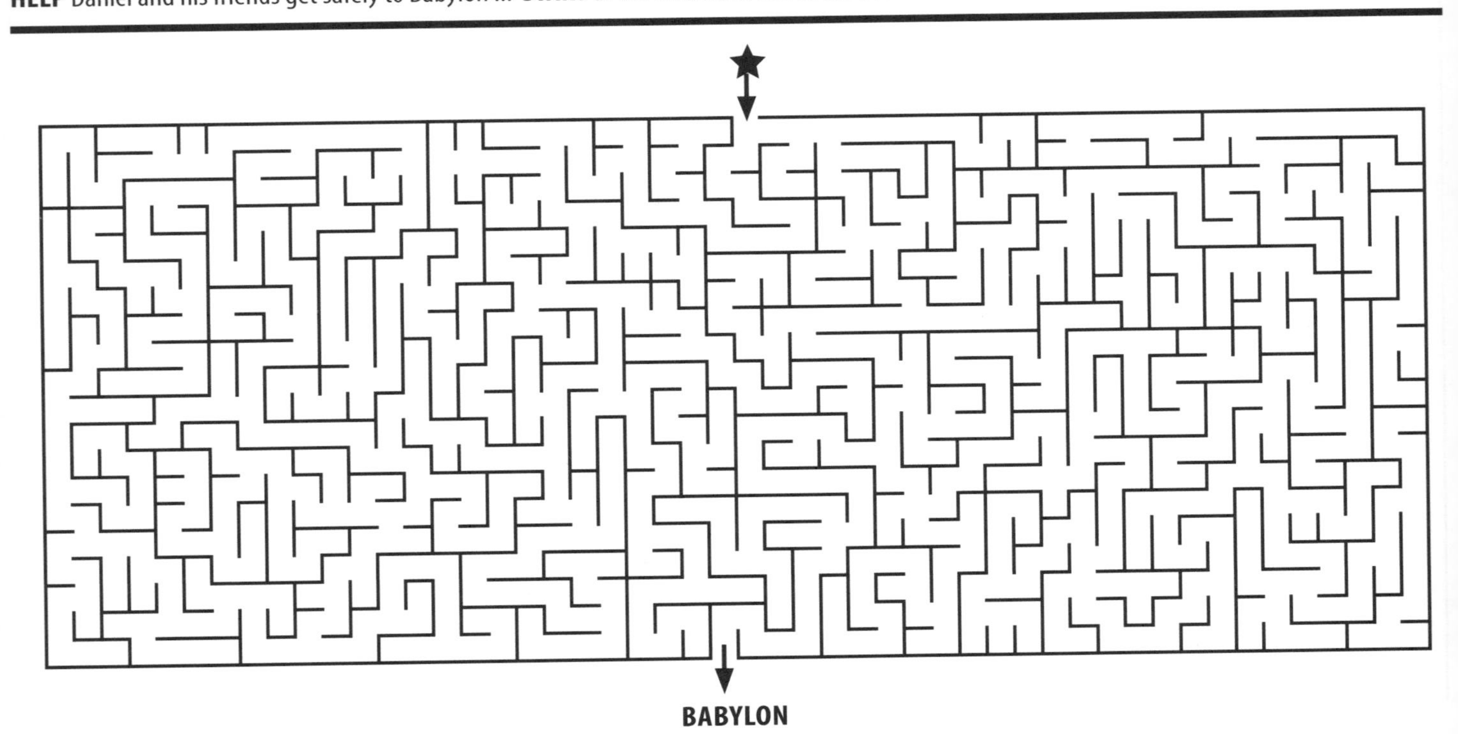

READ the **Picture Bible** pages 515–533.

COLOR this picture of Daniel in the lions' den. Notice that he is praying and that God sent an angel to protect him!

Day 19
JEREMIAH in Salvation History

Jeremiah was a prophet who tried to get the people to repent and stop sinning... but the people wouldn't listen to him. So, God allowed the Babylonians to invade and conquer them. **WATCH** the Jesse Tree VIDEO—it shows a lot of kids acting out the Babylonian invasion. It was fun for the Adventure Guides, but in real life, it was not fun for the Jews! We have only a few more days of Advent left, so Jeremiah's message to repent is a good one for us.

READ about it in the book of **Jeremiah chapter 31.**

After you've watched the video, take this **QUIZ** about Jeremiah and the Israelites!

1. Why did Jeremiah warn the Israelites to repent?
   a. They were worshipping false gods and not obeying God's laws
   b. They wasted their money on foolish things
   c. They didn't obey the Babylonians well enough

2. What important building did the Babylonians destroy when they captured the Israelites?
   a. Jeremiah's house
   b. The Temple
   c. The White House

3. What did Jeremiah say that God had promised to do for the Israelites?
   a. Make a new covenant with them
   b. Send them manna when they were hungry
   c. Repair the Temple for them

Now is also a good time to look back at your Advent so far and to plan for the remaining days until Christmas.
LIST some things you are going to DO —especially during these last days of Advent—to help others:

What I will do...

____

____

____

Whom I will help...

____

____

____

READ the **Picture Bible** pages 493–508.

COMPLETE the Bible quotes **CROSSWORD** below. (All the quotes are from Jeremiah chapter 31.)

ACROSS

5 "Not like the ________ which I made with their fathers..."
8 "My _______ which they broke,"
9 "But this is the __________"
11 "When I took them by the hand to bring them out of the land of ________,"
13 "Though I was their husband, says the ______."
14 "For they shall all know ___,"
15 "With the House of _________"
17 "Which I will make with the House of _______"
20 "From the least of them to the ______,"

DOWN

1 "I will make a new ___________"
2 "And no longer shall each _____ teach his neighbor..."
3 "and I will remember their ____ no more."
4 "And the House of _________,"
6 "And each his _______,"
7 "And I will be their ________,"
10 "And they shall be my ________."
12 "And I will write it upon their _________;"
13 "After those days, says the _______:"
16 "Saying, 'know the _______' "
18 "Says the _____; for I will forgive their iniquity,"
19 "I will put my _____ within them,"

WORD BANK:

You will use some words more than once.

brother
covenant
Egypt
God
greatest
hearts
Israel
Judah
law
Lord
man
me
people
sin

Day 19a

Angels, Angels Everywhere!

Have you noticed how many times in the Bible God sends angels as messengers? God sends angels to speak to you, too—and you have a special Guardian Angel whom God has sent to protect you during your entire life. Ask your guardian angel to help you every day. **WATCH** the **SPECIAL** Jesse Tree today about angels.

Everyone who was present on the night Jesus was born had been invited by angels! **COLOR** the picture of Jesus and His family and the angel!

READ the **Picture Bible** pages 88, 511, and 556–557

HELP the ANGELS!

God sent angels to tell several different people about Jesus.
Do you know remember whom?

Solve the maze below to find out!
Connect the ANGELS to the people.

(It's tricky—more than one path works!)

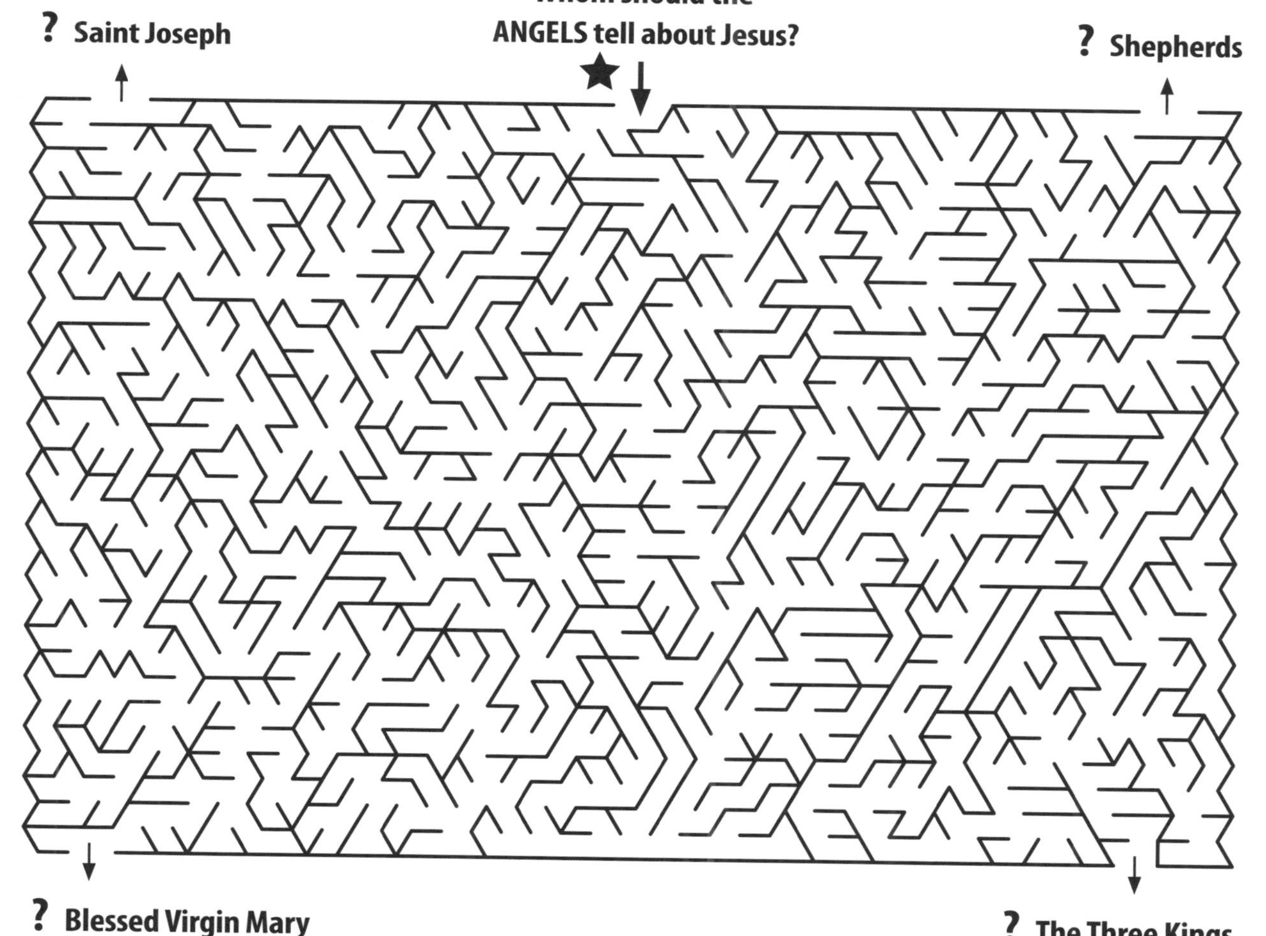

Day 20

Zechariah, Elizabeth, and John the Baptist

WATCH today's video about Zechariah, Elizabeth, and John the Baptist. Zechariah was a priest during Jesus's time and Elizabeth was his wife. They were old and could not have any children, which made them very sad. One day, the angel Gabriel appeared to Zechariah and said his wife would soon be pregnant and they were to name the baby John. Zechariah wouldn't believe the angel and asked for proof. Gabriel punished Zechariah by saying he wouldn't be able to speak until all the promises came true. Zechariah and Elizabeth did have the baby, and we know him now as John the Baptist!

READ about it in **Luke chapter 1.**

COMPLETE this **CROSSWORD**—it contains many of the things we've learned this Advent!

WORD LIST

antiphon
Christian
coal
Elijah
Elisha
Elizabeth
Epiphany
Gabriel
Gaudete
Goliath
Isaac
Isaiah
Jesus
Lucy
Magnificat
Melchior
Nativity
radiant
raven
red
roses
serpent
seven
Solomon
temple
tree
unclean
Visitation
Zechariah

ACROSS

1 Archangel who appeared to Zechariah.
5 Where the 12-year old Jesus was found.
6 What do we call the day we celebrate the visit of the Three Kings?
11 Isaiah said that he had _____ lips.
12 Decorate your Christmas tree with _______, not pagan, ornaments.
14 A _______ tempted Adam and Eve.
15 The name of the giant David killed.
17 The third Sunday of Advent is called _______ Sunday.
19 Who was the prophet who foretold the birth of Jesus?
21 This bird brought food to Elijah.
23 Cousin of the Blessed Virgin Mary.
24 An angel touched Isaiah's mouth with a burning_____.
25 The Second Joyful Mystery.
27 Christmas is the birthday of _____.
28 The father of John the Baptist.
29 The Third Joyful Mystery.

DOWN

2 The O Antiphon for Dec 21 is, "O ____ Dawn."
3 How many "O Antiphons"are there?
4 What color does the priest wear on martyrs' feast days?
7 This is a short verse said before the Magnificat during Vespers.
8 One of the Magi.
9 This prophet came right after Elijah.
10 This is the prayer Mary said when she went to visit Elizabeth in the Second Joyful Mystery.
13 This color of vestments is worn only twice per year.
16 Who was the son of Abraham and the father of Jacob?
18 The Christmas _____ is a symbol of the Tree of Life.
20 _______ built the Temple in Jerusalem.
22 _______ told the Israelites to stop worshipping Ba'al.
26 Saint _____ was a virgin martyred by the Romans for being a Christian.

READ the **Picture Bible** pages 546–553. **COLOR** the picture of Jesus talking about his cousin, John the Baptist.

As they were going off, Jesus began to speak to the crowds about John, "What did you go out to the desert to see? A reed swayed by the wind? ... Then why did you go out? To see a prophet? Yes, I tell you, and more than a prophet. This is the one about whom it is written: *Behold, I am sending my messenger ahead of you; he will prepare your way before you.* Amen, I say to you, among those born of women there has been none greater than John the Baptist; yet the least in the kingdom of heaven is greater than he." (Matthew 11:7, 9-11)

Day 21

The BLESSED VIRGIN MARY in Salvation History

WATCH today's "Jesse Tree" video—it tells the story of the Blessed Virgin Mary, the person closest to Jesus Christ from the moment of His conception until His death on the Cross!

Think about what it must have been like for Mary and St. Joseph as it got closer and closer to the time for Baby Jesus to be born! They were the parents of the King of the Universe!

The **Blessed Virgin Mary** wants to help you... and one way to do it is by helping you pray the **Rosary**!

We want to help you, too. That's why we have already filled in all the letters from the word "rosary" wherever they appear in the crossword.

ACROSS

2 Elizabeth called Mary the "_____ of my Lord."
3 Prayed 10 times each rosary decade (2 words)
4 Nazareth is in this region
7 The 2nd Joyful Mystery
8 Gabriel told Mary to call her son this name
9 This Joyful Mystery mentions all 3 Persons of the Trinity
10 The 1st Joyful Mystery
13 Gabriel is this
19 The "Hail, Mary" has this Archangel's greeting
20 Mary's son will have the ______ of his father David
21 The Magnificat is prayed during this
22 Mother of John the Baptist

DOWN

1 Gabriel said Jesus' Kingdom would last this long
2 This prayer is said during Vespers
3 Mary's son will rule over the _______ of Jacob
5 Gospel records 1st & 2nd Joyful Mysteries
6 Joseph was of the "house of _____"
8 Elizabeth lived in this region
11 Reminds us of Jesus becoming a baby in Mary's womb
12 Gabriel appeared in this town to Mary
14 All generations will call Mary _____
15 "Behold, I am the ______ of the Lord"
16 Mary was betrothed to him
17 When she heard Mary's greeting, Elizabeth was filled with the Holy ______
18 We use beads to count our ______ in the rosary.

It is getting very close to Christmas! Think about the Blessed Virgin Mary and Saint Joseph. They did not know what it would be like to have a baby in their family—and this would be not just any baby, but the Son of God, whom they had to protect and care for.

Your parents had to protect and care for you when you were a baby, too. **ASK** them to tell you what they did to prepare for the day you were born—they were loving you and taking care of you before they could even see you!

COLOR the picture of the Blessed Virgin Mary and Saint Joseph below.

An angel of the Lord appeared to Joseph in a dream. The angel said, "Joseph, son of David, do not fear to take Mary your wife, for that which is conceived in her is of the Holy Spirit; she will bear a son. And you shall call his name Jesus, for He will save His people from their sins." (Matthew 1:20-21)

Day 21

The BLESSED VIRGIN MARY in Salvation History

We call the mother of Jesus by many different names: Our Lady of Guadalupe, Our Lady of Fatima, and others. But all the names still refer to the same person.

Think about it: your own mother is sometimes called by her first name, or a nickname, or even just Mom!

What name did the Blessed Virgin Mary use with Saint Bernadette in Lourdes, France?

SOLVE the WORD SEARCH to find out what she said!

L	O	U	R	D	E	S	M	A	R	Y	S
A	I	L	A	B	A	N	N	E	U	X	B
D	S	A	N	S	I	S	I	R	A	P	E
M	O	S	N	Q	W	A	M	T	O	P	A
O	K	A	O	U	H	O	E	U	U	I	U
T	O	L	D	E	M	F	R	L	Y	M	R
H	T	E	A	E	A	L	A	R	C	U	A
E	O	T	M	N	A	D	A	T	O	L	I
R	E	T	A	D	A	S	T	E	I	S	N
C	H	E	Y	U	O	O	N	C	E	M	G
P	T	T	G	R	I	K	N	O	C	K	A
P	O	N	T	M	A	I	N	O	N	,	”

WORD LIST

Banneux	Mother
Beauraing	Our Lady
Fatima	Paris
Guadalupe	Pontmain
Knock	Queen
La Salette	Rosary
Lourdes	Sorrows
Madonna	Theotokos

There's a secret message in this word search!

When you have found all the words in the WORD LIST above, circle the **UNUSED LETTERS** in the grid and put them in order into the blank spaces below to find out what the Blessed Virgin Mary told Saint Bernadette at Lourdes!

Fill in the blank spaces below with the unused letters to find out what the Blessed Virgin Mary told Saint Bernadette!

___ ___ ___ ___   ___ ___ ___ ___,

“___   ___ ___   ___ ___ ___   ___ ___ ___ ___ ___ ___ ___ ___ ___ ___

___ ___ ___ ___ ___ ___ ___ ___ ___ ___ ___ ___

MARY is QUEEN of ALL SAINTS. How many saints in the picture below you can name? **WRITE** their names on the lines provided below.

(If you need **HELP** you can visit **HolyHeroes.com** and search for **Glory Stories Audio CDs** to see pictures of all the saints below.)

Day 21a
The BLESSED VIRGIN MARY visits her cousin!

Today's Jesse Tree video is about the Visitation! That's when the Blessed Virgin Mary visited her cousin, Elizabeth!

Why did Mary go to visit Elizabeth? ________________________________

Who told Mary that Elizabeth was pregnant? ________________________________

Use the map on this page to help you trace the path from each Joyful Mystery of the Rosary to the next, and think about who was there when these Mysteries occurred.

The 1st Joyful Mystery: The ______________
Where did it occur? Mark that place **#1** on the map!
Name the 2 persons present for this Mystery:
______________ and ______________

The 2nd Joyful Mystery: The ______________
It occurred in the town named Ein Karem marked **#2** on your map —there is a beautiful Catholic Church there today!
It is over 70 miles from Nazareth—wow!
At least 4 persons were present for this Mystery—name them!
____
____

The 3rd Joyful Mystery: The ______________ *(The first Christmas!)*
Where did it occur? Mark that place **#3** on the map!
Who was present for this Mystery? ______________, ______________, and ______________

The 4th Joyful Mystery: The ______________
Where did it occur? Mark that place **#4** on the map!
List the 5 persons present at this Mystery *(hint: see Luke 2:22-38)*!
____
____

The 5th Joyful Mystery: Finding Jesus in the ______________
It occurred at the same place as the 4th Joyful Mystery—so add **#5** to that place on the map!
Besides the teachers in the Temple, who else was present at this Mystery?
____
____

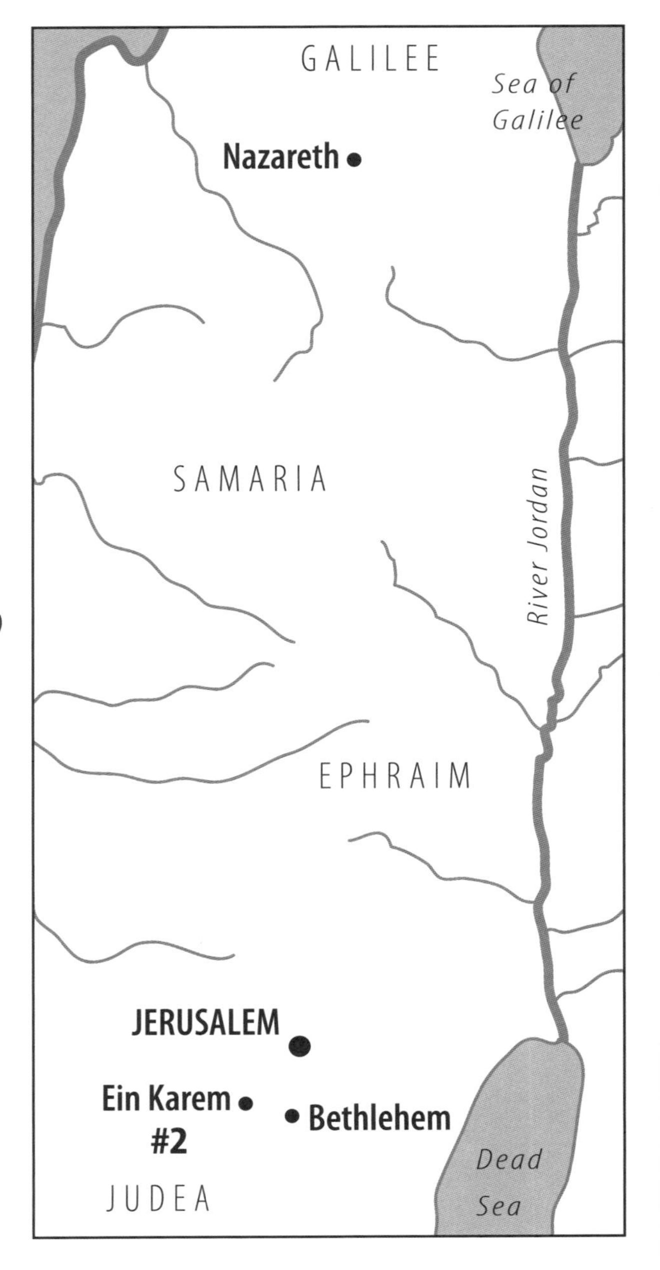

READ the **Picture Bible** pages 550–551.

OLOR the picture of the **Visitation** below.

When Elizabeth heard the greeting of Mary, the babe leaped in her womb, and Elizabeth was filled with the Holy Spirit, and she exclaimed with a loud cry, *"Blessed are you among women, and blessed is the fruit of your womb."* (Luke 1:41-42)

Day 22

JOSEPH, Mary's Husband and Foster Father of Jesus

Saint Joseph was the man God chose to be the foster father of His Son on earth. Joseph was a caring husband to Mary, a loving father to Jesus, a hard-working craftsman, and the protector of the Holy Family.

CONNECT the DOTS to complete this picture of Joseph and Mary. Imagine the joy they felt after the angel told him to take care of Mary and Jesus.

READ the **Picture Bible** pages 563–565.

After you have **WATCHED the VIDEO**, take this **QUIZ** below about Saint Joseph!

1. When is St. Joseph's (the Husband of Mary) feast day?
   a. March 19
   b. October 1
   c. January 2
   d. May 1

2. What is St. Joseph the patron saint of?
   a. Grandparents
   b. Fathers and husbands
   c. Good in-laws
   d. Charities and orphanages

3. The Bible does NOT tell us about St Joseph's ___________:
   a. Visions of angels
   b. Spoken words
   c. Obedience to God's Will
   d. Marriage to Mary

4. St. Joseph's ancestors were who?
   (Hint: there is more than one!)
   a. David
   b. Ruth
   c. Saul
   d. Daniel

You can get a **BIG 17-page coloring download** of the **Life of Saint Joseph** now at **HolyHeroes.com!**

You will find the pictures are a great summary of what we've learned this Advent about the Joyful Mysteries of the Holy Rosary!

Day 23

The First CHRISTMAS

We just talked about St. Joseph, and now it's time to think about the Holy Family! **WATCH** today's Jesse Tree video and you'll learn all about how Jesus was born.

Mary and Jesus had to travel a long distance to Bethlehem for the "census." The Roman emperor made everyone register so he would know how many people he ruled. While Mary and Joseph were in Bethlehem, they couldn't find any rooms, so they had to stay in a stable. That night, Mary gave birth to Jesus. The very first Christmas took place in a stable! That's why you usually see Baby Jesus placed on hay in a little manger.

Today's **WORD SEARCH** below is jam-packed with words that remind us about the first Christmas. Can you **FIND** them all? When you are done, **TELL** your Mom & Dad what all the words remind you about!

C S A H R S I S T I S B O R N C
Y E N R J E P J E S U S R Z G H
M H N T B I J R J R M T V J P J
R T A S E R J L V Z J W T T L Q
T O S O T E F W N F R V K M Z L
F L O N H T S D R E H P E H S P
H C H O L S N N Z L F N M J Q Y
T G T F E Y F N Z R N N O W R T
S N B D H M N L A L F S T A M M
L I T A E L Z E J T E C M T G W
E L J V M U L Z M P I A R K T T
G D B I L F X M H E I V S D D K
N D M D X Y X L H R S G I T M G
A A B B X O L P O K T I Y T A K
R W Y H F J B L F Y K T W L Y R
N S X C T N G S T A B L E T F P

www.WordSearchMaker.com

WORDS TO FIND

Angels
Bethlehem
Gloria
Hosanna
Jesus
Joseph
Joyful Mysteries
Mary
Nativity
Shepherds
Son of David
Stable
Star
Swaddling Clothes
Wise Men

Words can go horizontally, vertically and diagonally in all eight directions.

READ the **Picture Bible** pages 554–558.

It's time to COLOR the picture of Baby Jesus!

When you are done coloring, you can carefully **CUT** Him out along the dotted line. Then you can **MAKE** a manger out of a shoebox lid and line it with soft pieces of yarn. Place Baby Jesus in the soft yarn on Christmas morning!

A SUGGESTION:
Tape a piece of cardboard to the back to make Him more sturdy.

ANOTHER SUGGESTION:
***BEFORE** you cut out Baby Jesus turn the page to see our Christmas Day message to you and your family!*

Christmas Day!

Have a very blessed Christmas Season!

It's time to **COLOR** the Manger Scene above and **CELEBRATE** the birth of the **BABY JESUS!**